Published 2012. Pedigree Books Ltd, Beech Hill House, Walnut Gardens, Exeter, Devon EX4 4DH
books@pedigreegroup.co.uk www.pedigreebooks.com

The Pedigree trademark, email and website addresses, are the sole and exclusive properties of Pedigree Group Limited, used under licence in this publication.

Contents

£7.99

Welcome
to Lalaloopsy Land

Welcome to Lalaloopsy Land, the fantastical world where the Lalaloopsy dolls live. The Lalaloopsy are very special because they started out as ordinary rag dolls, but when their very last stitch was sewn, they came to life, as if by magic.

The special scraps of fabric used to make each doll, shaped her

personality. Turn the
page to meet and make
friends with everyone...

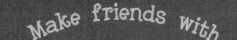

Hi, I'm Crumbs Sugar Cookie. Do you like biscuits and cupcakes? If you have a sweet tooth, you must come to my tea party. I was sewn on National Cookie Day, so I bake the best cookies around! You can reply to my invitation on the next page. Don't forget to let me know your favourite sweet treat so I can bake it especially for you.

My friends say:

I'm sweet and have perfect manners. I always remember to say please and thank you.

Sew Sweet!

Crumbs Sugar Cookie™

She was made from a piece of baking apron. She is super-sweet, has perfect manners and loves inviting friends over for tea and treats. She has a pet mouse.

Sewn On Date: December 4th
On National Cookie Day

You are invited to... my tea party...

on Saturday PM at...... my house......

Please come!
Love and kisses,

Crumbs
Sugar Cookie

✂ ·······························

I would love to come to your party!

My favourite sweet treat is

·····································

Love From

·····································

9

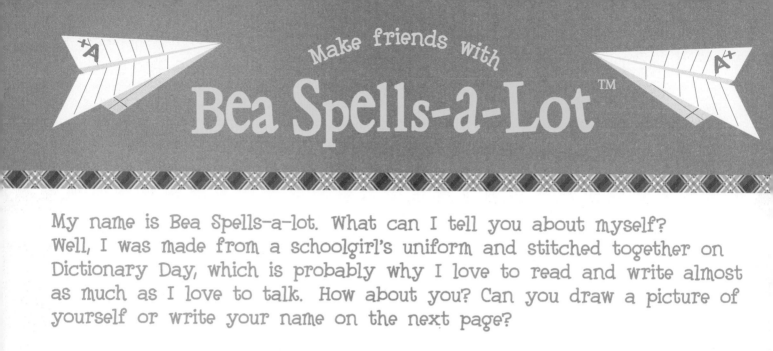

Bea Spells-a-Lot™

My name is Bea Spells-a-lot. What can I tell you about myself? Well, I was made from a schoolgirl's uniform and stitched together on Dictionary Day, which is probably why I love to read and write almost as much as I love to talk. How about you? Can you draw a picture of yourself or write your name on the next page?

Sew Smart!

Bea Spells-a-Lot™

She was made from a school girl's uniform. She is a real smartypants, who always follows the rules and loves to talk. . . A LOT! She has a pet owl.

Sewn On Date: October 16th on Dictionary Day

© MGA

My friends say:

I'M A CLEVER, CHATTERBOX who always follows the RULES.

This is me:

This is my name:

....

SMARTYPANTS

Tangle-tastic

CRUMBS SUGAR COOKIE has BLOWN UP a LOT of BALLOONS FOR her friends BUT she wants to save the YELLOW one for her pet mouse.

A B C D E F G

Which string should she pick to pull it down?

12

Bea Alert!

This is Bea's home, isn't it lovely? Colour in each of the seven objects along the bottom of the page as soon as you spot them in the picture.

Bea was here

ABC 123

stop

stop

2

5
3 2 4
1

13

Button Friendship Bracelet

You'll be cute as a button with this beautiful bracelet. It's colourful, quick to make and makes a lovely present for a friend. Just follow Jewel's simple step-by-step guide.

"Making things is a lot of fun, but scissors and pliers are sharp so ask a grown-up to help."

You Will Need . . .

- Elasticized cord
- Metal crimp tubes (available from craft shops)
- A selection of standard holed buttons
- Scissors and a pair of pliers

© MGA

What to do ...

Cut enough cord so it is long enough to wrap around the wrist twice.

Take your first button and thread the elastic from the back, through one hole and back out of the next. If your button has four holes, put the thread through two on the diagonal.

Repeat with the next button and continue until you have enough buttons to reach around the wrist.

Thread both ends of the elastic through the crimp tube and squeeze it tightly with pliers.

Trim the excess elastic with the scissors.

YOUR BRACELET IS READY. NOW why not make Button Bracelets for all your Lalaloopsy loving friends.

Lalaloopsy™ Story

PARTY TIME!

Jewel Sparkles was going to visit her friend Crumbs Sugar Cookie. Crumbs was the best baker in Lalaloopsy Land. Jewel couldn't wait to taste Crumbs' newest creation!

pARTy TiME!

Well, what do you think?" Crumbs asked. "I just perfected my recipe for strawberry-surprise cupcakes."

"Mmmm. These are your best yet!" Jewel said. "I have an idea. What if we threw a party and invited all our friends? That way everyone could taste your yummy cupcakes."

"Great idea!" Crumbs agreed. "Maybe our friends would want to help us plan the party, too."

Crumbs and Jewel's first stop was Bea Spells-a-Lot's house. "Hi, Bea. Guess what?" Crumbs said. "We're planning a party!" "I love parties. And I love to write," said Bea. She also liked to talk a lot. "I can make invitations and a fun sign, too."

story continues
PAGE 28

19

Dot Starlight™

She was made from a real astronaut's space suit. She's a dreamer who loves science, and she's always got her head in the clouds. She has a pet bird.

Sewn On Date: July 20th on the First Man on The Moon Day

Greetings friend! Dot Starlight here. Did you know that I was sewn from a real astronaut's space suit to celebrate the First Man on the Moon Day? Join the dots on the next page to find some of my favourite things.

Sew Starry!

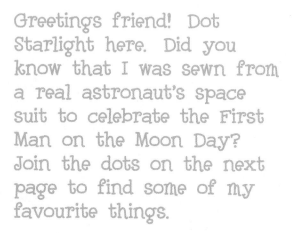

My friends say:
I always have my eyes on the skies and my head in the clouds.

Dot Starlight

Spot Splatter Splash™

Hi there! I'm Spot Splatter Splash and I've got my clothes messy again. I bet you can guess what I've been up to from the bright blue splotches on my pinafore. I was stitched together on famous artist Picasso's birthday, and I share his love of painting. I've just splashed myself while painting a picture of the button trees in Lalaloopsy land. Can you finish the picture with your brightest pens?

My friends say:

I'm amazingly arty and mightily messy.

Spot Splatter Splash™

She was made from a painter's overalls. She is super creative, and loves bright colors, big messes, and eating spaghetti.

She has a pet zebra.

Sewn On Date: October 25th on Picasso's Birthday

© MGA

Sew Creative!

22

Park

Spot Splatter Splash

23

Lala-locks

© MGA

Mittens and Jewel are the best of friends; Jewel loves Mittens' blue pigtails while Mittens admires Jewels pretty, pink ringlets. Use pink and blue pencils to give the girls a taste of each other's hair colour. Now, which other colours would suit them? Don't forget their bows and tiara too!

Spot and Dot the Difference

Spot Splatter Splash™

Dot Starlight™

Can you spot eight differences between these two pictures of Spot Splatter Splash and Dot Starlight? When you find each difference, draw a circle around it and then colour in a button.

Lalaloopsy Story
PARTY TIME!

Next, Jewel and Crumbs went to see Peanut Big Top.

"Hi, Peanut!" Jewel said. "We're having a party. Want to come?"

"I love parties," Peanut said. "Could I put on a show?" "What a delicious idea!" Crumbs replied.

Jewel and Crumbs visited Pillow Featherbed next.

"Pillow, wake up," said Crumbs gently. "We're planning a party. Is there anything you'd like to bring?"

Pillow yawned. Then said, "I can bring some fluffy cushions so everyone has a comfy seat." "Fantastic!" Jewel said.

Next Crumbs and Jewel went to Dot Starlight's house.

"Do you like this song?" Dot cried over the loud music. "Definitely! It will be perfect for the party we're planning!" Jewel said. "Sounds like a blast." Dot said, "I can't wait!"

pop

Lalaloopsy Story
PARTy TiMe!

Jewel and Crumbs went to see Spot Splatter Splash next.

"We're planning a party!" Jewel said. "Since you're such a great artist, maybe you could make some decorations?"
"Of course!" Spot said.
"I've got lots of creative ideas!"

"Jewel, we almost forgot about you!" Crumbs said.

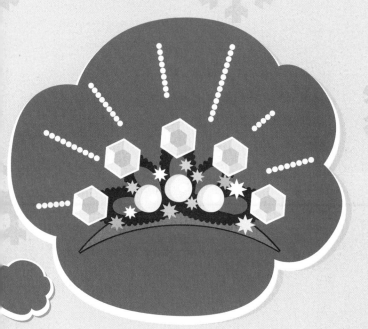

"What would you like to bring to the party?"
"I like to dress up for parties. So I'm going to make everyone a glittery tiara!" said Jewel.
"Great idea!" Crumbs said.

Their last stop was Mittens Fluff 'n' Stuff's house.
"Hi, Mittens. We're planning a party!" Crumbs said.
"What can I do to help?" Mittens asked.

"Whatever you're good at," Jewel replied. "I like to dress up for parties, so I'm making tiaras."

"And I love to bake, so I'm making cupcakes," Crumbs explained.

"I like snowflakes, icicles, and flurries. But I can't bring those to a party," Mittens said.
"Maybe I'll just help you instead."

story continues

PAGE 48

31

Jewel Sparkles™

My friends say:
I'M VERY GRACEFUL...
But a Bit Bossy sometimes.

So pleased to make your acquaintance. I am Jewel Sparkles and I was fashioned from material used to make a princess' gown. With my pink tiara and the frills on my beautiful dress, I'm always ready for the ball... or a party with my friends. The next page is covered with all the princessy things I love; can you circle the odd items?

Sew Sparkly!

Jewel Sparkles™

She was made from remnants of a real princess' dress. She is very graceful, a little bossy, and loves to dance and wear sparkly clothes. She has a Persian cat.

Sewn On Date: March 13th on Jewel Day

Stop

A+

Mittens Fluff 'N' Stuff™

Mittens Fluff 'N' Stuff™

She was made from pieces of an Eskimo's scarf. She loves hot cocoa, snow fights and snuggling by the fire.

She has a pet polar bear.

Sewn On Date: December 21st on the First Day of Winter

Sew Cosy!

Brrrr! It's freezing outside. But that's just the way I like it because I was made on the First Day of Winter from an Eskimo's scarf. My pet polar bear and I are never happier than when we are outside sledging and having snowball fights. Our favourite thing of all is when we lie down flat in the snow, wave our arms and legs up and down and make lovely snow angels. Use the next page to draw a snowy scene or a Lalaloopsy snow doll!

© MGA

My friends say:

I'm a fresh air and fun times kind of friend.

Sewing Square

There are ten sewing words hiding in this square. When you find them, tick them off the list below...Good luck!

© MGA

L	E	S	T	I	T	C	H	L	L	L
S	E	S	C	I	S	S	O	R	S	S
A	F	E	I	T	Y	O	N	N	E
F	T	F	R	Y	W	E	T	O	W
E	H	E	C	N	L	B	U	T	T
T	I	T	H	C	O	U	S	S	O
Y	M	K	N	I	T	T	I	N	G
P	B	U	I	T	W	T	T	O	P
I	L	T	H	M	I	O	O	O	L
N	E	L	D	E	E	N	N	L	C

- ■ Button
- ■ Cotton Reel
- ■ Knitting
- ■ Needle
- ■ Safety Pin
- ■ Scissors
- ■ Sew
- ■ Stitch
- ■ Thimble
- ■ Wool

36

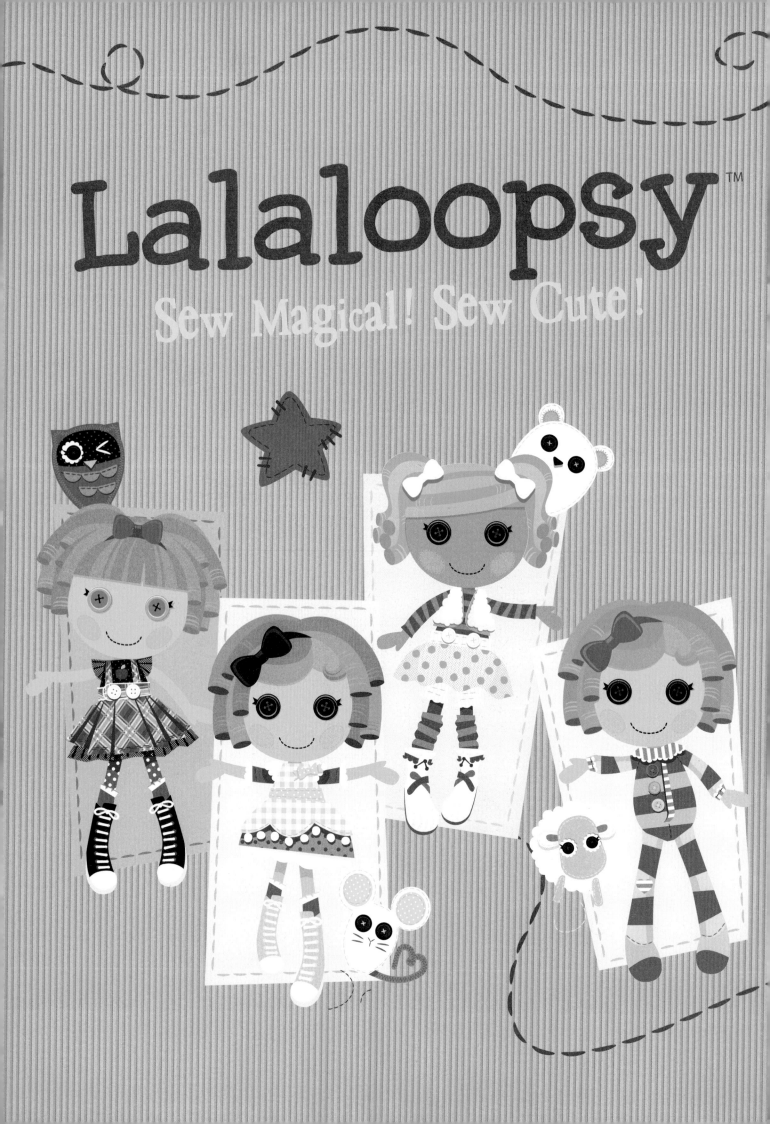

Sew Sweet!

A-Maze-ing

Oh no! Dot's house has blasted off into the blue without her. Can you help her find a route through the clouds to get home?

 Use your finger or a pencil to trace the path.

41

Concentrate

Time to see if your memory is as good as Peanut's pet elephant! Ask a grown-up to time you, as you look at this picture of Crumbs outside her super sweet home. Give yourself two whole minutes to drink in every detail.

© MGA

Now cover up the picture and see if you can answer these ten questions.

1. How many trees are there in the picture?

....

2. What is at the top of Crumbs' chimney?

....

6. Which shape is on the front door, a heart or a flower?

....

7. How many clouds are in the sky?

....

3. Which place does the sign point the way to?

....

4. Who is closest to the house, Crumbs or her pet mouse?

....

5. How many windows does Crumbs' house have?

....

8. What is there hanging from one of the clouds?

....

9. What colour is Crumbs' hairband?

....

10. Is there a full moon?

....

Hello, I'm Pillow Featherbed. I'm feeling pretty sleepy, but before I go for my nap I've just got time to tell you about myself. The reason I look so snuggly is because I was sewn together on the Festival of Sleep Day, from pieces of a baby's blankie. Do you have a favourite toy you take to bed? Use the next page to tell me all about it. You could stick in a photo, draw a picture or write about why it always shares your bed.

Sew Snuggly!

My friends say:
I'm cute, cuddly and huggable.

Pillow FeatherBed™

She was made from pieces of a baby's blankie. She loves good stories, long naps, and her favorite snack is milk and cookies. She has a pet sheep.

Sewn On Date: January 3rd on the Festival of Sleep Day

© MGA

ZZ Z...

Pillow FeatherBed Loves Cookies & Milk

Pillow FeatherBed Loves Cookies & Milk

milk

My best bedtime snuggle buddy is called...

....

He/she is a...

....

I love him/her because...

....

He/she looks like this...

Make friends with Peanut Big Top™

Roll up, roll up...to meet me – Peanut Big Top. I was sewn together on April Fool's Day from scraps of a costume which belonged to a circus clown. I'm so colourful and silly that I'll always put a smile on your face. Look, my pet elephant even wears a top hat! He's brilliant at balancing – can you draw him on top of the balls?

My friends say:
I'm sunny, smiley and silly.

Peanut Big Top™
She was made from a brightly-colored clown costume.
She is a silly prankster who's a little bit clumsy and loves to make her friends laugh.
She has a pet elephant.
Sewn On Date: April 1st
On April Fool's Day

Sew Silly!

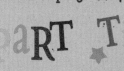
PaRT TiMe!

Crumbs tried to teach Mittens how to make cupcakes. But Mittens' cupcakes didn't come out quite right.
"I'm not as good at baking as you are," Mittens said sadly.
"Maybe I'll help with Jewel's tiaras instead."

Jewel showed Mittens how to decorate tiaras, but Mittens' tiaras didn't come out quite as nice as Jewel's.

"I'm no good at making tiaras either!" Mittens cried as she ran home. "I'll be the only one who didn't help with the party!"
Jewel and Crumbs found Mittens at her house. She was very upset.
"Everyone has a special talent but me," Mittens sniffed.
"That's not true, Mittens," said Crumbs.
"You're great at lots of things," said Jewel.

"I'm great at building snowmen, but I can't bring a snowman to the party. . . . Wait a minute — that's it! Snow!"
Jewel and Crumbs looked at each other. "Huh?"
"I'll explain later," said Mittens. "I've got a great idea!"

"Looks like everything is ready," Spot said as she put the finishing touches on the decorations.

"But we are missing one very important thing — " Crumbs added. "Mittens!"
"I hope she comes," Peanut agreed. "It just wouldn't be the same without her."

Just then, someone knocked at the door. "Mittens!" Jewel cried. "You came!"
"I sure did! And I brought an extra-special treat," Mittens said proudly.

PARTY TiME!

story continues
page 68

51

1-2-Bea

Clever Bea just loves numbers and this is her favourite type of colouring activity. Each number in the picture has been given its very own colour. Look at the key below to see which colour to use for each numbered area of the picture on the right. So for example, use your blue pencil to colour every section of the picture, which has a number one in it.

© MGA

"Your colouring is exemplary!"

A+

Pillow's Best No Bake Cookies

Pillow loves cookies with her milk and these are her favourite because, as they don't need baking in the oven, they're simple to make and ready in a flash. Kindhearted Crumbs is always ready to whip up a batch for Pillow to enjoy.

You will need . . .

- 450g white sugar
- 40g unsweetened cocoa powder
- 120ml whole milk
- 100g butter
- 1 teaspoon vanilla extract
- 1 pinch salt
- 100g chunky peanut butter
- 500g quick cooking oats

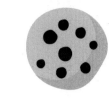

© MGA

"Remember to ask an adult before using the kitchen because knives are sharp and pans are hot!"

© MGA

In a saucepan over medium heat, combine the cocoa, sugar, milk and butter.

Bring to a boil, stirring occasionally.

Boil for 1 minute.

Remove from the heat and stir in the salt, vanilla, oats and peanut butter.

Using dessert spoons, dot rounded spoonfuls onto a baking sheet lined with greaseproof paper.

Allow the cookies to cool for at least 1 hour.

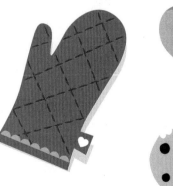

Have a Lalaloopsy Day!

Why not throw a Lalaloopsy Day for your Lalaloopsy-loving friends. The dolls have some great ideas for things to do!

Crumbs Says:

BE THE PERFECT HOSTESS

The secret of a good party is preparation, so be sure to have fun planning your guest list, menu and decorations. You could blow up coloured or spotty balloons, make colourful paper bunting or paint paper plates to look like buttons and thread them through with bright organza to hang them up. Throw a scrummy tea with fruit juice and sandwiches – Spot likes jam and Peanut loves peanut butter! Oh and don't forget the cookies and cupcakes!

Bea Says:

USE YOUR HEAD

I like games which use your brain. Memory games are really fun. Ask an adult to put 8 different items on a tray and let you look at them for 2 minutes before covering the tray up. How many will you remember? You could give a prize for the person who remembers the most items.

Spot says:

GET CREATIVE

Colouring is such fun. Lay out your brightest pens and pencils and some blank paper and ask your guests to draw their favourite Lalaloopsy. Or you could ask a grown up to find you some printable colouring pages online.

Jewel says:

FANCY DRESS

We all love the chance to dress up, so why not ask your guests to come in their prettiest party dresses, princess or fairy costumes or, to dress up Lalaloopsy style with spotty frocks and stripy socks or tights!

Dot says:
EYE SPY

I love looking at the sky at night, But there are lots of games you can play outside in the daytime too. How about I spy or cloud gazing, where you lie on your backs and try to see funny shapes in the clouds? Try spotting shapes which look like our pets — a mouse, a cat, an elephant etc.

Peanut says:
PUT ON A SHOW

Now you're all dressed up, why not put on a spectacular Lalaloopsy show. Think up an exciting adventure for us all, give everyone a part and then act it out. Remember, we all have very different personalities, so there's a part for everyone.

Big Show Tonight!

pop

Mittens Says:
WRAP UP WARM

This is my favourite party game because it involves lots of the things I have in my wardrobe, plus a big bar of chocolate. You'll need a pair of gloves, a big scarf, a hat and a pair of ski goggles or sunglasses. You will also need a big bar of chocolate, a tray and a knife and fork.

1. Put the unwrapped bar of chocolate and knife and fork on the tray in the centre of the room. Place the pile of clothes beside it.

2. Now sit in a circle surrounding the clothes and the tray.

3. Take turns to throw the dice. Pass the dice to the next person unless you have thrown a 6.

4. If you throw a 6 you still pass the dice to the next person and the dice continues around the circle — meanwhile you rush to the centre of the circle, put on all the clothes and then use the knife and fork to start eating the chocolate. Remember you only have until the next 6 is thrown so get munching.

5. Meanwhile the others continue throwing the dice until the next person throws a 6 and then they rush to the middle take the clothes from the person who's been eating, put them on, pick up the cutlery and start munching, etc.

6. Keep going until the whole choccy bar is in your tummies!

Pillow Says:
RELAX

At the end of a fun day, it's nice to relax. You could all sit down and watch a movie — maybe our brilliant new DVD adventure, where I get lost — or just have a break and drink a mug of hot chocolate or warm milk before you go off to bed.

milk

Dot to Dot

CRUMBS has arranged a special surprise for her friend Dot today.
She's taking her on an adventure. Join the dots to find
out what the excited pair and their pets are up to.

58

Lalalolly Game

Yum! Crumbs Sugar Cookie loves the scrummy lollipops which grow out of the ground all over Lalaloopsy Land. Can you work out which lollipop should come next in each of these grassy meadows? Pick from the pictures at the Bottom of the page and write the letter in the space.

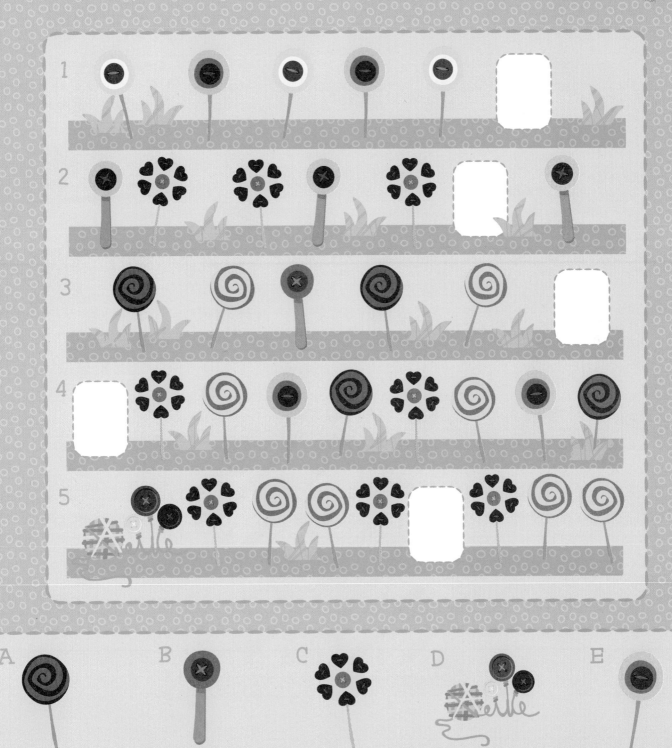

Home Sweet Home

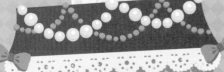

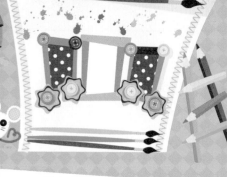

This house belongs to...

This house belongs to...

This house belongs to...

Today the Lalaloopsy have been playing 'house swap'. They've each spent the day living in a friend's house. Can you match up each of the dolls with her real home? Draw lines between house and owner or write the owner's name in the space below her actual home.

This house belongs to...

Once Upon a Time... Forever After

This house belongs to...

This house belongs to...

Paint with Spot Splatter Splash

Splatter art is super messy and super fun. It's also really easy to do. Here's how to paint up a storm just like Spot Splatter Splash.

You Will Need . . .

- Selection of coloured paints – eg. poster paints.
- Small Paintbrush
- A drinking straw
- Large sheet of white paper
- Sheets of Newspaper (to protect the surface you're working on)

"Don't forget to ask a grown-up before painting and put on an apron or overalls to keep your clothes clean."

What to do . . .

Cover the surface you're working on with old newspaper to keep it clean.

Place your white paper on the newspaper.

Dip your brush in the paint and then flick the paint at the paper so it splatters across it.

Repeat this with lots of different colours, washing the brush out in water whenever you use a new colour.

If you like you can create even more patterns by blowing bigger spots of paint around on the canvas using the drinking straw.

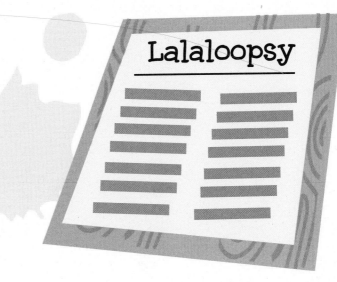

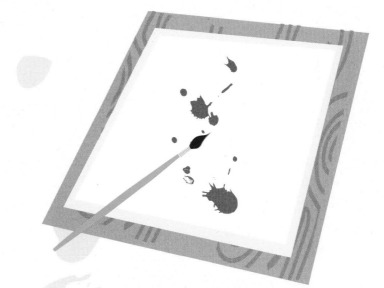

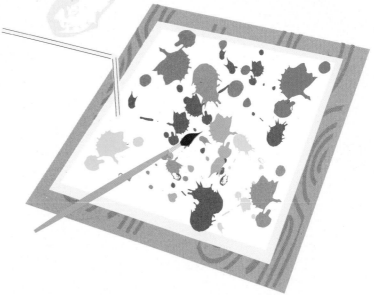

"Art comes from the heart"

BONKERS
Bunting

It's Perfect Pet Day in Lalaloopsy Land and the dolls are having a party for their loyal animals. They have sewn special bunting but it's got jumbled up in the breeze. Look at the letters and then put them in the right order.

U S O M E

N A H E T P E L

B R I D

Snoozy Colour Copy

Pillow's been playing all day and now she's really tired. Can you move her into bed by copying the detail in each square of the picture on the left, into the same square in the grid on the left?

© MGA

"Let me sleep on it!"

"Would you like to try my triple-mint snow cones?" Mittens asked.
"Absolutely," Crumbs exclaimed. Then she took a bite. "Yum! No one could have made these better than you!"

Because everyone worked together, the party was a hit!

Bea's invitations let everyone know where to go.

Spot's decorations made the party look cheerful, and all the girls looked festive because of Jewel's beautiful tiaras.

PARTY TiMe!

The girls danced to Dot's music. Then they watched Peanut put on a juggling show. Finally, the girls sat back on the cushions that Pillow brought and snacked on Crumbs' cupcakes and Mittens' snow cones.

"This was the best party ever!" Mittens said when the party was over. "I had so much fun."
"And your snow cones were a hit!" Crumbs said.
"They're cool," Jewel added.
"And sweet — just like you!"

The End!

The Talent Show Trail

The dolls are racing to meet their pets at the annual Lalaloopsy Pet Talent Show. Cut out the counters from the bottom of p77 and grab a dice. You'll need one counter for each player.

START

1

2

3

4
MISS A TURN WHILE SPOT SKETCHES YOU.

"keep perfectly still!"

FINISH

TALENT SHOW!

TALENT SHOW!

21

20

19
MOVE FORWARD ONE IF YOU CAN SAY WHICH HAIR ACCESSORY SPOT WEARS – A HAIRBAND OR BOWS?

7

CRUMBS HAS LEFT A CAKE IN THE OVEN. RUN BACK TO SQUARE 1 TO WARN HER.

8

9

10

YOU TRIP OVER PEANUT'S UNICYCLE. MISS A GO

"Move forward 3 if you can say the alphabet and 6 if you can also say it Backwards!"

11

6

12

BEA'S OWL IS HOOTING, MOVE FORWARD 2 IF YOU CAN HOOT IN REPLY

13

SWITCH–A–STITCH!

CHANGE PLACES WITH ANOTHER PLAYER

5

MOVE FORWARD 1 IF YOU CAN SING PILLOW A LULLABYE.

14

15

TRY JUGGLING LIKE PEANUT

17

Once Upon a Time Forever After

18

SLEEPOVER AT PILLOW'S HOUSE – GO BACK 4!

16

MOVE FORWARD 5 IF YOU KNOW WHAT CRUMBS IS SEWN FROM

Happy Holidays!

Christmas in Lalaloopsy Land is sew magical — of course the crisp, cold weather makes it my favourite season, But I also love the twinkly fairy lights, Bright green holly, yummy gingerbread — made by Crumbs — and brightly wrapped presents. Why don't you give a friend or family member a Lalalovely surprise with one of these cute greetings cards?

You Will Need . . .

Piece of A4 card, folded in half to give A5 size.

Scissors and Glue

Glitter

What to do . . .

Carefully cut around the dotted lines to cut out the picture.

Glue the picture onto the front of the folded card.

Paint glue around the edge of the card and then carefully shake glitter onto it, to create a sparkly border. It's a good idea to do this on a tray to keep the glitter from spilling everywhere.

Leave the glue to dry and then shake the card over the tray so that any excess glitter falls off and can be easily swept up.

Now write your greeting inside. You could write 'Wishing you a Lalaloopsy Christmas' or 'Happy Holidays'.

© MGA

See You Soon!

Thanks for stopping by and remember you can catch up with us all at www.lalaloopsy.com for more adventures, games and fun.

© MGA

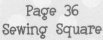

L	E	S	T	I	T	C	H	L	L
S	E	S	C	I	S	S	O	R	S
A	F	E	I	T	Y	O	N	N	E
F	T	F	R	Y	W	E	T	O	W
E	H	E	C	N	L	B	U	T	T
T	I	T	H	C	O	U	S	S	O
Y	M	K	N	I	T	T	I	N	G
P	B	U	I	T	W	T	T	O	P
I	L	T	H	M	I	O	O	L	L
N	E	L	D	E	E	N	N	L	C

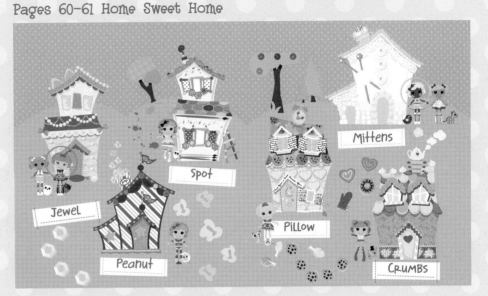

Mittens
Spot
Jewel
Pillow
Peanut
CRUMBS

The Talent Show Trail

Cut out the counters with the faces of Dot, Peanut, Jewel and Mittens for the The Talent Show Trail on pages 72-73

You'll need one counter for each player.